To Joe and Hannah – for surviving my
wilderness walks

You do not need to read this page –
just get on with the book!

EAST SUSSEX SCHOOLS LIBRARY SERVICE	
16-Feb-2009	PETERS
1215048	

First publ...

18 W... ...ter St, Edinburgh, EH1 2LR

Barrington Stoke Ltd

www.barringtonstoke.co.uk

ISBN: 978-1-84299-609-6

Printed in Great Britain by Bell & Bain Ltd

Contents

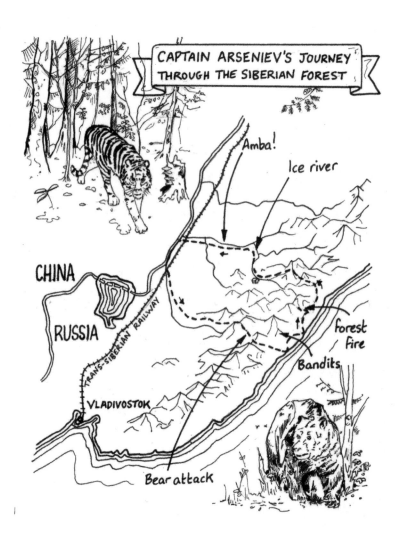

Chapter 1
A Stranger on the Trail

Things were not going well. Captain
Vladimir Arseniev and his small group of
soldiers were wet through from the rain.
They had been bitten all over by mosquitoes
and their skin itched like mad. A week
before, when they had been crossing a fast
flowing river, their horses had almost been
swept away. It was only by luck that they
had saved the horses, and the boxes of food
that they had been carrying. Then one of

their boats had flipped over and they had lost half their guns in the water.

They had tried to light fires around their camp, but these had gone out. So many insects had died in the smoke that they had fallen into the flames and put them out. To make matters worse, the men were now in tiger country. Each time they stopped to make camp, sleep was impossible. The horses would not settle. They were too scared.

The Captain ordered his men to go on. If the weather got better, they would be able to hunt deer or wild boar to eat. Maybe there would be grass for the horses. With the rivers so high from all the rain, going back was not an option.

Captain Arseniev's mission was to explore and draw maps of the mountains and coast-line of South-eastern Siberia. Russia had been given this land by the Chinese as part of a peace treaty. No-one in Russia really knew what was there. All Captain Arseniev knew was that it was an area of wilderness with thick forests and wild rivers called the *Taiga*. There were tigers, wolves and bears. And there were gangs of armed robbers. That's why Captain Arseniev and his three assistants needed a platoon of soldiers – Cossack riflemen – to protect them.

The Cossack soldiers were famous horsemen. They were the toughest men in the Russian army. This lot had been specially picked for their ability to live off the land. Right now it was raining again and the soldiers had begun to grumble. They were lost. They were wet. They wanted to go home. Also, they were feeling on edge. As they trudged through the dark forest, every crack of a twig or rustle in the leaves had them reaching for the triggers of their rifles

– a small bird, the wind moving the tree tops, a man!

He was right up close before the soldier at the front had time to grab his gun. The stranger was armed. He held a long-barrelled *Berdianka* rifle in his hands. It was pointed down. The man wasn't about to shoot.

The soldier relaxed – just a little. By the look of him, the stranger was an old native from the Gold tribe. He lived by hunting wild animals and by finding forest plants. Most likely he lived in a shelter made of birch bark. He was wearing a deerskin shirt and leggings, and a cloth tied over his head – like a pirate. This Gold tribesman was smoking a long clay pipe.

The Captain's dog, Alpa, came running up from behind, barking. The woodsman held out his hand and the dog started licking it.

"Morning, Captain," he called out, and at that, the soldiers burst out into smiles and started laughing. They knew now that the man was Dersu Uzala, the famous tracker, the guide they had been looking for. This was the man who, two years ago, had saved their Captain's life in a snow blizzard. With Dersu to lead them through to the coast, they had nothing to worry about now.

Chapter 2
Dersu

Dersu's bush-craft skills in the *Taiga* forest were famous. He could track any animal from the smallest sign. He could tell from foot marks, droppings and even a scratch on a tree-trunk, how long ago an animal had passed by, and whether it was running or feeding. Dersu always knew if there were people nearby. He pointed out old foot-prints, scraps of cloth snagged on thorns, and bark (stripped off the trunks of birch trees) that would show if a hunter's hut was close. (Hunters flattened the bark out like cardboard to make roof tiles for their cabins.)

To Dersu, everything was alive. To him, fire, water and even the wind were all different men.

"He chatter a lot," Dersu would say if the campfire crackled and spat sparks. "Give him dry wood to eat then he happy."

If there was a storm it was because the wind was angry.

Dersu was one of the last living members of the 'Gold' tribe. He was a native of Siberia who had grown up here in the *Taiga* forest. Once he had a wife and children, but they had died of the disease smallpox. Now he was alone. He carried everything he owned in his back-pack. Captain Arseniev once saw what Dersu had in his pack. There was just a bedroll, two old shirts, a pair of moccasins for his feet, and some things for making bullets. There was a horn full of gun-powder, lead balls, cartridge cases and a box of percussion caps for setting off the bullet's gunpowder charge.

Dersu was a crack shot. He always kept his old *Berdianka* rifle with him. When Captain Arseniev offered to swap him a new, better one, he said, "no way". He knew exactly how a bullet flew from his gun. With it he could take down a deer at long range, even if it was hidden in the bushes. There was one animal he would never shoot at though. That was *Amba* – the tiger. He had his own special reason for that.

Chapter 3
Amba

Three days later. On the trail again. Still raining.

Dersu stopped and pointed at the ground. There in the mud right in front of him was the four-toed foot mark of a tiger. It was right on top of a soldier's boot print made only minutes before.

"He here now." Dersu looked left and right then dashed back along the trail twenty steps or so. There were more tiger tracks right over where he and Captain Arseniev had just walked.

The Captain could see that Dersu looked scared. The soldiers were way out in front. The Captain and Dersu were alone. No help would come if the tiger attacked. Dersu loaded his rifle. His fingers were trembling. Out of the corner of his eye, Captain Arseniev caught sight of something big moving behind the bushes. He swung his head round for a better look. It was hard to tell if those were tiger stripes or just lines of shade between the tree trunks and branches.

Suddenly Dersu put his arms out wide, waving his rifle in the air, and yelled out to the forest.

"Why do you follow us, *Amba*? What do you want?"

"This is a big place. Plenty of room for you and us."

The two men stood still and waited, their eyes scanning round to see if anything moved. Nothing stirred. Captain Arseniev could no longer see the stripes behind the leaves.

The Captain relaxed. The danger had passed – or so he thought. But, that night he found out that tigers aren't so easily scared off. When Dersu took him to a marsh to hunt a deer for supper, the tiger *Amba* was waiting.

The two men were hidden at a place from where they could get a clear shot at anything that moved. The moon hadn't yet come up. It was pitch black. But, though they couldn't see the deer, Dersu could hear it coming closer – and that was enough for him to hunt it. In his mind Captain Arseniev could picture the great stag that was now approaching. He could hear the deer's soft foot-falls and the sound of water rippling as it moved through the marsh. Dersu followed the movement with the barrel of his rifle.

"Grrrr!"

The tiger's sudden growl – so close by – seemed to pass right through the two hunters. Captain Arseniev felt himself tense up and his mouth go dry. His legs felt heavy. He wanted to run but he knew he would not be able to move.

"Grrrr!" The tiger growled again.

Dersu put down his rifle and stood up.

"All right, *Amba*," he said to the unseen tiger. "This is your place. We not know. No be angry."

Dersu went down on his knees and bent his head down low as if he were praying. And then, pulling the Captain with him, he hurried away.

Later Dersu explained the reason for his terror.

"Me see *Amba* much. One shot I took at him missed. Now me very much fear. For me now one day will be bad, bad luck."

Dersu had once shot at the tiger *Amba* and he was sure that one day *Amba* would get his revenge.

Chapter 4
The Bear Hunt

They had no more run-ins with tigers over the next few weeks. Dersu, who knew all the hunting trails in the area, led the Captain and his soldiers over the mountains and down towards the coast.

At times they met people. Mostly these were Chinese men dressed in blue, hunters of Ginseng (a plant used to make medicine). Some were trappers looking for small mammals called *sable* whose sleek fur they could sell. These people were often scared of the soldiers. They had heard of a large gang of bandits raiding the farms near to the coast and so didn't trust anyone who looked like a stranger.

While the soldiers led the pack horses, Captain Arseniev would go off with Dersu to study the local wildlife – and sometimes hunt it for the men to eat! Mostly they were successful, bringing back a wild boar or a Roe deer for the next meal. But, sometimes there was trouble. On one night, when they were hunting, Captain Arseniev mistook Dersu for a wild boar and shot him in the back. (Luckily the bullet hit Dersu's gun strap and only gave him a blood blister.) Another time hunting, it was the Captain who nearly got killed.

He was tracking a brown bear and had him in his sights. Normally he wouldn't hunt bear for food but the men hadn't eaten well for days and this animal looked an easy target. The bear was rooting round the forest floor and hadn't seen him. The Captain took aim and fired. The bear swung around, biting at the place where the bullet had hit, as if it had been stung by a bee. The bear was still very much alive. And angry now. It spotted Captain Arseniev – and charged. With lightning quick reactions, the Captain slid another bullet into the rifle, and shot again. The bullet hit, but the bear was still coming. In panic, Captain Arseniev started to run, frantically trying to reload as he zigzagged through the trees. He skidded to a stop, sunk to one knee, lined up the gun. The bear was almost on him. Its huge body filled his gun sight. Captain Arseniev could see the bear's eyes and its slobbering mouth.

Kaboom! He loosed a shot off. The rifle belched smoke and the bear crashed over, but the Captain kept running.

Suddenly there was a bear behind the bushes to his side.

"How can it be?" the Captain gasped out aloud. "I shot it three times. I saw it go down." And as he dropped down onto the ground, he realised the truth. This was another bear.

There was a chance that this second bear had not seen him. Its head was still down, its nose sniffing out food in the fallen leaves. Ever so slowly the Captain began to crawl away from the snuffling animal, and then he legged it.

After a while, when he felt calm, he crept back towards where the first bear had fallen (after all, his men still needed meat). He found tracks – his own, and the scrape marks in the earth where he fired his third shot. But the bear was not there.

Leaves rustled behind him. Captain Arseniev was ready for yet another bear. He spun around, gun pointing.

It was Dersu.

"It's over there," Dersu said, ignoring the rifle pointed at his face. Then, pushing the Captain's gun to one side, he nodded towards a large pile of freshly dug earth.

"Other bear bury body. We must dig it up quick and take it before he gets back."

Chapter 5
Bandits

It was early summer by the time the explorers reached the coast. Here there were rivers full of fish. The waters were teeming with salmon on their way up-stream to spawn. The sea cliffs were loud with nesting birds and the beaches with honking sea lions. There were also more signs of people. Mostly they were farmers and trappers, but then one day, when Captain Arseniev and Dersu were scouting way out in front of the rest of the group, they found a set of tracks that looked far more sinister.

Next to some boot prints on the muddy trail Dersu saw a scrap of blue cloth and a half-smoked cigarette stub. This hadn't been chucked away by some poor woodsman, he pointed out. This was a man who could afford to waste tobacco.

A short way up the trail, the tracks of three more men joined those of the first.

"Bandits?" Captain Arseniev suggested.

Dersu wasn't sure. He said he would go on alone and have a look.

The Captain hid himself in the bushes just out of sight of the path and waited. Twenty minutes went by, then an hour. He was getting worried. Suddenly, in the distance, there was a scream and four gunshots rang out, one after the other. Captain Arseniev readied his rifle. Nothing. Everything was quiet. Then he heard running feet pounding towards him and Dersu appeared. He was covered in slimy mud and was panting. In his shirt there was a neat hole where a bullet had gone through the cloth but just missed his body.

"We go now," he wheezed and ran on.

The two men fled back to a wide river and made camp in the open from where they could get a good view of anyone approaching. There, Dersu told his story. He said he had found a camp. There were 20 or so armed Chinese. Bandits. He had thought he was well hidden, but a dog had smelled him out and started barking. Three men had picked up rifles and chased after him. Normally Dersu would have been able to slip away, but he had stumbled into a marsh and by the time he had pulled himself out, the men were nearly upon him. He had shot the first man.

Then he had gone back on his tracks towards the camp, trying to give the other two men the slip. They had fired at him as he made his get-away.

Captain Arseniev was worried. He hoped his Cossack guards would come looking for him and Dersu before the bandits got to them. But by sunset they had seen no-one, friend or foe. The Captain and Dersu spent a cold and sleepless night, not daring to light a fire in case the bandits saw it.

In the morning, Captain Arseniev and Dersu set off to find the soldiers. They kept away from trails. After a few hours they came across a Chinese hunter. He was clearly scared stiff at the sight of the two armed men stepping out the forest. He held his hands high in the air, and then he pulled something out of his shirt. It was a letter from the Cossack soldiers saying that the Captain and Dersu were to go with him. The soldiers were in a nearby valley, staying as so-called 'guests' of Chan Bao, the warlord.

Chapter 6
The Warlord

The warlord looked at the Captain and Dersu and gave out a string of orders which his armed guards snapped to obey. He was Chinese, about 45 years old, with long greying hair and a drooping moustache. Captain Arseniev thought he had the look of someone used to power. *Maybe*, the Captain wondered, *Chan Bao had once been an important officer back in China. Maybe he had committed some crime and was now on the run. Was he really the leader? And if he*

was, did that mean that Dersu and himself were now prisoners?

The Captain need not have worried. When Chan Bao's men came back, they were carrying steaming bowls of food. The warlord was a friend after all.

Once Captain Arseniev and Dersu had eaten, Chan Bao asked them about the bandits that had chased them. How many were there? How were they armed? And where exactly was their camp?

He said he had heard of these bandits before. They had arrived in boats a few nights ago. Perhaps they were planning to attack one of the Chinese 'Junk' sailing ships that traded along the coast. Now that these bandits had shown they were hostile, Chan Bao made up his mind to stop them straight away before they attacked his people's villages. He called over two of his men and gave out orders. Within minutes, his band of warriors was ready to leave.

With Chan Bao off hunting the bandits, Captain Arseniev thought it was safe enough to carry on with his expedition. He started making plans for how everyone would get back to their base in the city of Vlastivostok.

He decided that his three assistants and most of the Cossack soldiers would go back to the city by boat, taking with them the notes and the maps they had made on their journey. Meanwhile Captain Arseniev, Dersu and four of the strongest soldiers would attempt to return across the mountains by a different route. Autumn would soon come and soon the first snows would fall. Captain Arseniev knew that first he had to plan his route carefully and make some scouting trips to explore the best way to get across the mountains. When the time came to cross them, there could be no room for mistakes.

Chapter 7

Forest Fire!

When you travel through the wilderness it's often the small hazards that are the most dangerous to life. So far, the Captain had escaped bears and bandits. He and his soldiers had coped with the dangers of crossing flooded rivers. It was to be something far smaller that put his life most at risk.

A thorn went through his boot and stuck in his foot. He pulled it out but at the end of the day his foot was still red and painful. The tip of the thorn had broken off. It was still in there and it was getting infected. By the end of the third day, the Captain could hardly walk. His foot was so swollen that he had to use his knife to cut his boot open just to put it on. The infection was starting to spread up his leg and he had a fever. Captain Arseniev was in pain but his life, as yet, was not in danger. What was to put his life at risk was the forest fire.

Dersu saw it first, a curl of smoke above the trees with a red glow behind. He knew what it meant.

"Run," Dersu shouted. "Run to the river!"

But the Captain couldn't run. He could hardly walk. To make things worse, there were lots of fallen trees in this part of the forest. He had to crawl on his hands and knees to get through. Looking back, Dersu could see the heat sucking the air into whirl-winds that pulled branches and leaves into the flames. A fire-storm was starting. Captain Arseniev wasn't fast enough. He would never make it to the river before the flames got to him.

Dersu dropped his old *Berdianka* rifle – his favourite belonging – picked up the Captain and staggered into the shallow water. There was a bare patch of stones on the other side of the river. Dersu dropped the Captain there then sprinted back for his gun. When Captain Arseniev came-to a few minutes later, Dersu was covering both of them with the tent canvas, which he had soaked in the river.

Dersu had made it across just in time. Huge trees on the opposite bank were bursting into flames. Sparks were showering down and smoke was billowing out across the water. For Dersu and the Captain, sheltering

beneath a wet tent, the air was so hot and full of smoke that it hurt to breathe. How long this lasted, they couldn't tell. It was only a matter of minutes but it felt like hours. At some point the wind must have changed direction. The heat and the smoke and the sparks eased off and it seemed that they might live through this fire at last.

But what could they do next? There was no way that Captain Arseniev would be able to able to pick his way across the red hot ground where the forest fire had passed, let alone dodge the places where it was still burning. Dersu made up his mind to go for help. The Captain knew that was the right thing to do. Alone, Dersu had a chance of getting through. Together, that chance would be zero.

Every hour dragged like ten. To Captain Arseniev lying alone in pain at the river's edge the wait seemed endless. He watched as the fire which he thought had burnt out blazed up again. A large wild boar swam across and scuttled past him. A snake slid by. He lay helpless. When the pain of his foot became too much, he felt out where the infection was worst with the point of his knife and stabbed at it. A mass of yellow pus burst out and soon the pain got less. Still, he was out-cold again when Dersu arrived the next day with a man and his horse.

Dersu brought the Captain back to Chan Bao's camp. The warlord was angry because someone had told the bandits that he was coming after them and they had escaped in their boats before he reached them.

The four soldiers, still with the Captain and Dersu, were keen to start their journey home, but now they had to wait for the Captain's foot to get better. This delay was the last thing they needed. By the time the Captain and his soldiers set off across the mountains, Dersu told them that the snow was already on its way.

Chapter 8
Blizzard

Crossing the Sihote Alin mountains.

The six men had been trekking for a week now. The walk up into the mountains had gone well. It was Autumn, and all around them were fruits to be had. The rivers were full of salmon, which were dying after spawning. They moved slowly and were easy to catch. There were dead or dying fish at every bend of the river – and the crows,

eagles and bears that arrived to feast on
them.

Dersu looked worried. He said that the
weather was about to turn really bad.

"In morning, all the birds eat quickly.
Look, Captain! No can see birds now. Me
think better we should make camp here."

Even though it was late September, it still
felt like Summer. The sun was shining.
There were no clouds in the sky. It was hot.
The four soldiers looked to the Captain to see
what he thought of what Dersu had said.
Captain Arseniev thought that Dersu had got
it wrong this time but he said "yes" to
making camp anyhow.

Dersu said they should peg the tents
down extra well and collect a stack of
firewood. The soldiers grumbled at this.
They had hoped they would spend the
afternoon lazing in the sunshine.

That night the full moon shone with a strange rainbow halo around it. Everyone felt the temperature dropping.

"Now it begin," said Dersu.

Within seconds, a wind had started up, blowing snowflakes around the forest. Tree tops started to sway. Branches were breaking off. Then whole trunks were toppling. The full force of the blizzard hit. Tons of snow swirled around the huddling men covering everything and everyone. The men piled the wood they had cut onto their fire and sat closer together, now grateful for Dersu's warning earlier in the day. As they felt the temperature fall still lower, they all knew they would have died if they hadn't followed his instructions.

Next morning, the Captain looked out over the blasted forest. Broken trees, white with frost, stuck out of the snow. The ground

was rock hard. Captain Arseniev knew it would stay like that until next spring. He also knew that when the next lot of snow fell, the trek ahead would be hard for men without snow-shoes or skis. With this in mind, he hurried everyone forward. Soon they were over the highest peaks of the mountains and on their way down the other side. Dersu said there were Udege people, natives of Siberia like his own Gold tribe, living in the valleys ahead of them. The tribe might be able to help them with the next part of their journey.

Chapter 9
Ice River

Inside a wood and deer-skin wigwam.

The headman of the Udege tribe sucked on his long wooden pipe and thought about what the Captain had asked for. In the dark, smoky hut, Captain Arseniev thought the man looked just like an American Indian. The only difference was the fur cap he wore, which had a squirrel tail sticking upwards at the back. His wife, sitting next to him, had at first looked like she was about to run away into the forest. She had thought to herself, *Who are these six hard-looking men? Are they bandits?* But Dersu had spoken to her in her own language and told her that they were friends.

In the hut, it was Dersu who spoke first. He knew it was the Udege custom not to talk to strangers until they had told their story. He explained how Captain Arseniev had been sent by the government of Russia to make a map of the *Taiga* area. The headman then spoke. He said he had been expecting the soldiers for several days. His tribesmen had been tracking them. Yes – he looked at the Captain – he would take the men down the river in his boat if, in return, Captain Arseniev passed on a message for him to the government.

"The Chinese bandits make our young men hunt for them and then get them addicted to the drug Opium," he told the Captain. "You tell your government this and we will take you down river."

Captain Arseniev and his soldiers found travelling by river fast and easy. It was better than trudging through the snowy forest. Two Udege boatmen (one at the front, one at the back) did the hard work using long poles to push the large canoe along, while the soldiers could relax and enjoy the ride. The boatmen made the job look easy but the Captain could see from the looks on their faces how hard it was to get the over-loaded canoe around the rapids. Things were becoming harder because now ice was starting to form over the river's edges.

They soon arrived at a village that was the home of some Chinese traders and the Udege hunters who worked for them. Most of the Udege were drunk or addicted to Opium. The Captain could see that the traders were

treating the Udege people unfairly and wanted to get on with the journey. But his men needed to sleep and the traders' houses were better for that than camping out in the snow. It was two days before the group set off again.

Back on the river the rapids became more fierce. The weather got colder. Now there were parts of the river where the ice on each side nearly met in the middle. Sometimes huge slabs broke off and floated like icebergs with the current. They were going down the narrow channel of open water with the ice closing in on them. Suddenly the way was blocked! There was no way through.

The Udege desperately tried to pole the boat backwards. The soldiers helped by back-paddling with oars and their bare hands, but it was no good. A huge block of ice moved in to shut off the channel behind them. Suddenly they were trapped. Ice-bound! But not for long. Shock-waves from the iceberg's crash rippled along the ice shelves. The men watched in horror as cracks spread across the frozen surface. Everyone could see that if the ice broke the boat would be swept along too – and there were huge boulders at the next river bend.

"Ice soon break boat. Must go quick!" Dersu shouted.

He sprang into action. Grabbing a rope, he leapt out of the canoe onto the cracking ice and made for the river-bank. Twice the ice-shelf broke under him, plunging him into freezing water but he made it across. The Cossack soldiers tried next. Two of them leaped across the ice and onto the shore. A third soldier, called Murzin, was not so lucky.

The chunk of ice that he landed on rolled over. He went under. All his friends could see were his hands grasping for the ledge.

Then Dersu was in the water too, pulling him out. Meanwhile in the boat, Captain Arseniev and the boatmen were trying to stop a large iceberg from pushing past and crushing Dersu and the soldier Murzin. They held the iceberg back just long enough. The boat floated free for a second and the two men, drenched and frozen, clambered back into the boat. Then they were all swept down the river at a great speed.

In the frothing white water and mass of floating ice blocks, the boatmen had given up trying to control the canoe. It was every man for himself now. The two boatmen leapt for the side. Their two dogs followed, as did Murzin and the other soldiers. Dersu and Captain Arseniev were last out. Before they came, they threw out as many of the packs of food as they could. Then they jumped. Seconds later the canoe hit the rocks at the river bend and was smashed to pieces.

Now things went from bad to worse. Not only had they lost their boat but now the men were soaking wet in sub-zero temperatures. Much of their food and equipment had been lost in the river. They were miles from anywhere. The first thing to do was to get dry. Somehow Dersu managed to get a fire started and the soldiers set up a camp for the night.

The next day, they set off following the river down-stream. The snow was deep and it was hard going. The men hadn't eaten well for weeks. Everyone was feeling weak. What was left of the food ran out after two days, and with empty stomachs the men felt terrible.

When they saw some fish heads by the side of the river that had been left by a bear, they ate them raw. But that wasn't enough. Within a day the hunger pangs were worse than before. Dersu cut up some deer leather he had in his pack. He boiled it and the men ate the pieces. It was tough but at least it filled their stomachs. With everyone feeling so feeble, their forest senses were dulled. All the men – even Dersu – stopped seeing the signs that animals were around. More importantly they failed to realise that the forest's predators were hungry too – and that they had now become the prey.

Chapter 10
The Tiger's Revenge

Everyone was so tired when they made camp that no-one sat up to keep watch that night. The Captain pointed out that he could hear wild boar moving through the forest.

"Why are they moving around?" he asked Dersu. "You said boars don't travel at night."

"Other man hunt him."

Other man? The Captain struggled to understand. Did Dersu mean an Udege

tribesman? A Chinese trader? A Russian?
Then he realised. When Dersu said 'man', it
could mean the wind. It could mean the
snow. It could be – he sat up with a start –
the tiger *Amba*! The Captain dragged his
sleeping bag closer to the camp fire. Tigers
were supposed to be scared of flames. He
kept his rifle with him. He tried to stay
awake, listening for every rustle in the
leaves. He peered through the smoke into
the black outside the safety of the circle of
firelight. Every patch of shade might hold a
tiger and he had to be ready for it. But *Amba*
was silent and invisible, and try as he might
the Captain just could not stay awake.

Thud! He came-to suddenly as something
heavy landed on his chest. Claws were
scrabbling over his face. Fur was smothering
him. Acting on instinct, he pushed the
animal up and off. It was one of the Udege's
dogs. Now it stood its ground, head held low,
teeth bared, growling at the darkness.

What happened next was too quick to react to. Across the fire – which was just glowing – a second dog barked. Its last yelp was cut short. There was a deep growl, a tearing of undergrowth – and a tiger leapt into the camp. It was enormous. Its orange, white and black striped fur was dusted with snow. The dog was in its mouth, neck ripped open, blood pouring onto the ground. The tiger came to a stop right next to where Captain Arseniev was lying. Snug in his sleeping bag, his arms were pinned to his sides. He couldn't move – or was it that he was frozen with terror? He could smell the tiger's musky odour and make out every one of its whiskers around its muzzle. He could feel its electrifying presence in the camp – his camp. *Amba* sensed him too, and looked down. Their eyes met and for the Captain, time stood still.

This is it, he thought, *I'm going to die.*

Eye to eye, tiger to man, man to tiger. It was a fraction of a second that lasted forever. A drop of the dog's blood slowly slid down the tiger's chin and dropped onto the sleeping bag. Was *Amba* about to drop the dead dog? Was it about to come for him? Without blinking, Captain Arseniev stared up at the great beast and for some reason that he never could explain, he went calm. Somehow, he knew he wouldn't die tonight. Eye contact was broken. The dying dog twitched in the tiger's mouth. *Amba* tightened its grip on the dog, tensed its sleek back legs and sprung into the darkness.

Time re-started. *Quick! Gun, shoot*, the thoughts sped through Captain Arseniev's mind. He reached for his rifle. But there was no point. The tiger had gone. The Captain felt his grip relax. Dersu appeared – he didn't see where from – and grabbed the gun from the Captain's hands. Dersu shot it off into the air. He was angrier than Captain Arseniev had ever seen him before.

"*Amba*, you got no face," he shouted into the darkness. "You one big thief, worse than dog. Me no afraid of you. Another time I see you, I'll shoot to kill."

In the past, Dersu had once shot at and missed *Amba*. Now the tiger had attacked and missed him. In Dersu's mind, he and *Amba* were now even.

Two days later the Captain, Dersu and the four Cossack soldiers found a hunter's hut in the snow. From then on they had enough food to carry on. As they neared the town and the trans-Siberian railway line, which would get the soldiers back home, they all knew the expedition was at an end.

Together they had fought tigers, bears and bandits, and they had explored the unknown East coast. Captain Arseniev wanted Dersu to come back to the city with him, but the old hunter would not have it. He said he was afraid of towns and there was nothing he could do there.

"Me hunt for sable fur – it's the same as money to me," he said quietly to the captain. Then, accepting a gift of some bullets for his old *Berdianka* rifle, he set off once more into the *Taiga* forest that was his home.

Barrington Stoke would like to thank all its readers for commenting on the manuscript before publication and in particular:

Rose Chesney
Harry Cross
Amyleigh Drysdale
Callum Fraser
Nick Guise
Angela Hunter
Moira Kleissner
Jill Murray
Katie Helen O'Hara
Sarah Pybus

Become a Consultant!

Would you like to give us feedback on our titles before they are published? Contact us at the email address below – we'd love to hear from you!

info@barringtonstoke.co.uk
www.barringtonstoke.co.uk

Private – Keep Out!

Simon's Diary:

To the forests of Siberia

In 2006 Simon Chapman set off on a new trip – to search for the Snow Tiger ... turn the page for a secret look at the diary of a real-life explorer!

Victor, our driver looked like a pirate - big, strong with a bandana tied round his head. He kept a wooden baton and a 45 pistol by him at all times. I also saw he had an axe in the boot. Sergei said this was for self-protection.

A viper is spotted. 1 metre in length.

I found another tiger track! The tiger had walked behind the camp the night before, while we were sleeping.

Tiger Track

Same as my hand span

Mosquitoes are hell here. At night I un-zipped the tent to go for a pee. Dave woke up and came out too. We got covered in mosquitoes and filled the tent with them.

Dave says that next time I need a pee in the middle of the night I will have to use one of the old beer bottles.

This afternoon was scary. Back on the river, on one zig-zag rapid, a wave washed over us, filling the canoe with water. Then we hit a rock and swung side-on to the flow. I jumped onto the rock. Sergei almost fell out and we nearly capsized.

The canoe was filling up with water at one end and the dry bags (inside one of them was my passport) were starting to float off. I grabbed the bag, but then I fell in and was washed down with the current. I knew I had to float feet first so I didn't knock myself out on any rocks. I swam to shore then went back to help Sergei with the boat. I made it halfway across the rapids but the water dragged me away. I got a finger-hold on a big rock, pulled myself up to where Sergei was still holding the boat, and we got back in.

It hurt when I tried to breathe deeply for weeks afterwards. I think when I hit a rock, I broke one of my ribs.

A Snow Tiger's Skull

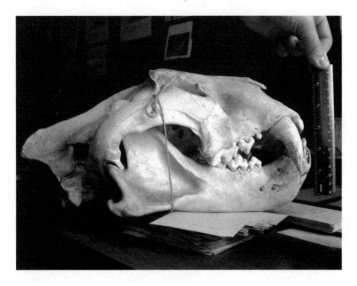

At the tiger reserve, a very keen enthusiastic taxidermist (someone who stuffs animals and birds) showed us his huge collection. Small birds like sparrows were stuck onto sticks a bit like lollies.

He pulled out one drawer of stuffed birds so quickly that he dropped around 20 cuckoos all over the floor by mistake.

Snow Tiger!

I got this photo from a man who reared tiger cubs. He also had bears that people had found and taken to him. He kept 3 tigers in a large zoo-like enclosure behind his house. He raised the money to feed the tigers by selling photos like this one.

He had become the leading expert in how to raise snow tigers in captivity. I think he had once been an academic who had chosen to leave the university where he worked to live on the edge of the forest and look after tigers.